Theory of Music Workbook

for Trinity College London written exams

Grade 1

by Naomi Yandell

Published by
Trinity College London
www.trinitycollege.com

Registered in England
Company no. 02683033
Charity no. 1014792

Designer and editor: Natasha Witts
Music processed by New Notations London
Printed in England by Halstan, Amersham, Bucks

Acknowledgements

Trinity College London would like to acknowledge the invaluable contribution to the development of this music theory programme by music teachers, professors, examiners, language specialists and students from around the world. Their comments have usefully informed the final shape of the workbooks and exam papers, and are much appreciated.

Grade 1 Theory of Music Syllabus from 2007

Section 1	General multiple choice – 20 questions	*(20 marks)*
Section 2	Writing scales and arpeggios	*(20 marks)*
Section 3	Correcting mistakes	*(15 marks)*
Section 4	Answering a given rhythm	*(15 marks)*
Section 5	Ostinato	*(10 marks)*
Section 6	Analysis – 10 questions	*(20 marks)*

Questions and tasks may cover:

Rhythm

1. Note values of semibreves, dotted minims, minims, crotchets and quavers (beamed in 2s, 4s or 6s only) using English terms (with an option to use American terms, e.g. minim or half note)
2. Rest values of semibreves (including semibreve rests showing a whole bar's rest in any time signature), minims and crotchets using English terms (with an option to use American terms, e.g. minim or half note rest)
3. Time signatures of $\frac{2}{4}$, $\frac{3}{4}$, $\frac{4}{4}$ and $\mathbf{C}$ (common) time
4. Grouping note and rest values above within $\frac{2}{4}$, $\frac{3}{4}$, $\frac{4}{4}$ or $\mathbf{C}$ (common) time

Pitch

1. Naming and using notes in treble or bass clefs (to one leger line above or below the stave)
2. Accidentals (the flat, the natural, the sharp)
3. Tones and semitones
4. C, F and G major keys, their scales, key signatures, one-octave arpeggios and tonic triads (root position)
5. Identifying the key of a piece in C, F or G major
6. Concept of numbers 1–8 being used to name degrees of the major scale
7. 1st degree of the scale being known as the tonic or doh
8. Degrees of the scale can be at different registers
9. Tonic triad labelled:
   – as a chord symbol above the music (e.g. C in the key of C major)
   – as a Roman numeral below the music (e.g. I in the key of C major)
10. Intervals (as a number only – unison, 2nd, 3rd, 4th, 5th and octaves above C, F or G)
11. Circle of 5ths relating to the keys above
12. Ostinato

Musical words and symbols

Dynamic and articulation marks

Pianissimo, piano, mezzo piano, mezzo forte, forte, fortissimo, accents, *crescendo, diminuendo, legato,* slurs, *staccato* (and signs and abbreviations for these where appropriate)

Tempo, expression marks and other words and signs

Andante, allegro, moderato, repeat marks, *ritenuto* (and signs and abbreviations for these where appropriate)

Introduction

Why write down music?

If you read a book you are reading another person's thoughts. If you play music you are playing another person's **musical** thoughts. People write books and music so that they can share their ideas.

Learning to read and write music is important because it helps musicians to play what is written down quickly and easily. Having said that, some brilliant musicians have never learned to read music. They play by ear. That's great, but if you want to play in bands and orchestras, or to write your own music, you need to learn to read and write music.

Using this workbook

The writing in the boxes ☐ tells you:

- About the music that you sing, or play on your instrument
- What you need to know to pass your Trinity College London Grade 1 Theory of Music exam

Doing the tasks

- Use a pencil with a sharp point and a fairly soft lead so that you can easily rub out what you have written if you need to

- Be careful to be accurate with musical notes and signs – this will make a difference to your marks because the examiner must be able to read what you have written

- Read through the boxes to make sure you understand how to do the tasks and ask for help if you need it

- The first task in each section has usually been done for you in red to show you what to do

- Use the pictures of the piano keyboards, including the one on page 53. They are there to help you, even if you do not play a keyboard instrument

- **Always try to play, sing or tap the music you write.** This is a very important part of learning, and will help you 'hear' what you write in your head. It will help you in the exam when you have to work in silence

What comes next?

When you have finished this book try some sample papers. You can purchase them from www.trinitycollege.com/shop. You will then be ready to ask your teacher to enter you for the Grade 1 Theory of Music exam.

The stave

Music is usually written on a set of five lines called a **stave**.

The **note-heads** (the oval-shaped dots shown below) can be put either on the lines, like this:

Or in the spaces between the lines, like this:

Handy tip!

Note-heads are oval, not round in shape.

1 Write a note-head on every line.
Leave gaps between the notes as shown in the examples above.

2 Write a note-head in every space.

3 Write three note-heads on the third line up from the bottom.
Then write three note-heads in the first space.

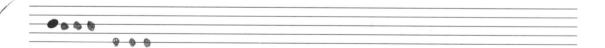

4 Write a note-head on every line and in every space.

Writing high and low notes

High notes are written near the top of the stave and **low notes** near the bottom. The lines coming from the note-heads are called **stems**.

As a general rule, if the notes are high the stems go down and if the notes are low the stems go up. The middle line is usually the only line where a stem can go up or down. This makes the music easy to read.

Keyboard players will know that on the keyboard high notes are usually played with the right hand and low notes with the left.

1 Add a stem to each note-head. Place each one carefully and keep the length of the stems the same as shown in the examples above.

Handy tip!

Put stems on the left of the note-head for high notes.

Put stems on the right of the note-head for low notes.

2 Add a stem to each note-head.

3 Write five high notes and five low notes using note-heads and stems.

4 Add a stem to each note-head.

Did you know?

Some note-heads are solid black and some are not.

Treble and bass clefs

Did you know?

People named notes using letter names as far back as the time of the Ancient Greeks.

To show exactly which high or low sound to play, each sound has a name. The letters used to name notes are **A B C D E F G**. They repeat themselves over and over again – higher and higher.

A **treble clef** (or G clef) is used for high notes. The little curved line in the middle of the clef curls around the second line where the note **G** sits:

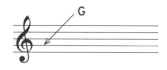

1 Write over the dotted lines to make treble clefs. Draw them as one continuous line.

2 Write five treble clefs. Check that the curved line in the middle of the clef curls around the second line.

A **bass clef** (or F clef) is used for low notes. (The little dots go on either side of the line where **F** sits):

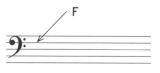

3 Write over the dotted lines to make bass clefs.

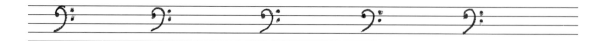

4 Write five bass clefs. Check that the dots go on either side of the line where **F** sits.

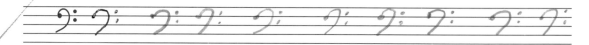

Middle C

Middle C is a note like any other. It has the word **middle** in front of it because it is in the middle of most keyboard instruments. In both the treble and bass clefs **Middle C** sits on a little line of its own (called a **leger line**).

In the treble clef it is written like this:

In the bass clef it is written like this:

Both notes mean **Middle C** and sound the same.

If **Middle C** appears in the treble clef in music for keyboard, the player usually plays it with the right hand – if in the bass clef, the player usually plays it with the left:

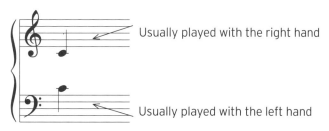

Usually played with the right hand

Usually played with the left hand

Handy tip!

Leger lines are written the same distance away from the stave as the stave lines.

1 Write three **Middle C**s in the treble clef.

2 Write three **Middle C**s in the bass clef.

3 Write in a treble or bass clef to make these notes **Middle C**.

Grade 1 notes

Here are the treble clef notes you need to know for Grade 1:

B Middle C D E F G A B C D E F G A B

Elephants Go Bananas Driving Fast

Learn these first:

Treble clef lines:

E G B D F

Treble clef spaces:

F A C E

You may like to think of words to help you remember these (for example, **E**very **G**reen **B**us **D**rives **F**ast).

1 Name these notes:

F E A D B F G B E C

G C C B E D E D F B

2 Write two different Ds.

3 Write two different Bs.

4 Write two different Cs.

5 Write two different Es.

Did you know?

If two notes have the same letter name but they are in different places on the stave, they are said to be at different **registers**. Listen out for notes at different registers next time you practise your instrument. The distance between one note and the next with the same letter name is called an **octave**.

Grade 1 notes 𝄢

Handy tip!

Test yourself by writing out every Grade 1 note on a separate sheet of paper and timing how quickly you can name each one.

All notes can be checked using the G in the G clef, the F in the F clef or Middle C.

Here are the bass clef notes you need to know for Grade 1:

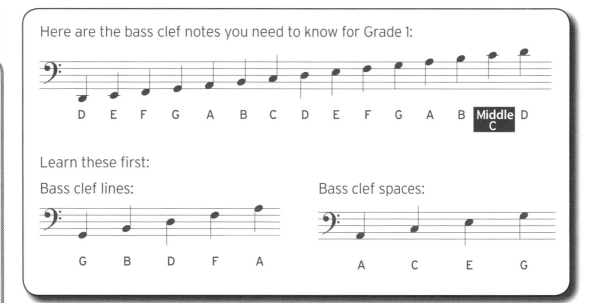

D E F G A B C D E F G A B **Middle C** D

Learn these first:

Bass clef lines:

G B D F A

Bass clef spaces:

A C E G

1 Name these notes:

A D F C G A B D G D

C A D E E G A E G B

2 Write two different Gs.

3 Write two different Cs.

Handy tip!

Check that you put the stems in the correct place.

4 Write two different As.

5 Write two different Fs.

1 Name the notes to find the hidden words.

B   E   D

F̶ E ̶E̶D̶
A   G   G   E

B A G

C A G E ✓

A   C   E ✓

B̶A̶ G G A̶G̶E̶
D C B B C B G

E   D   G   E

C A B B A G E ✓

2 Write notes to match the note names.

C   A   B

B   E   A   D

A   G   E

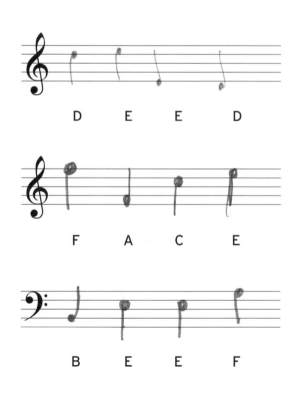

D   E   E   D

F   A   C   E

B   E   E   F

Note values

Did you know?

Sometimes other names for note values are used, especially in America. They are shown at the back of this book. You do not need to know them for Grade 1, but you can learn about them and use them in your exam if you want to do so.

Each note lasts for a certain length of time; musicians measure this time by feeling the number of silent regular beats within the note value. The beat used to measure notes in Grade 1 is the **crotchet**.

Notes are drawn in different ways to show how many beats to count while the note is played:

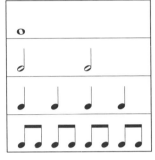

Semibreve   This note lasts for four crotchet beats

Minims   These notes last for two crotchet beats each

Crotchets   These notes last for one crotchet beat each

Quavers   These notes last for half a crotchet beat each. They are always beamed together for Grade 1 (see page 33)

   (crotchet beat)

The note that lasts for three crotchet beats is known as a dotted minim: 𝅗𝅥.

A dot after a note means that half its value again is added to its length, for example:

Minim (two crotchet beats) 𝅗𝅥		Crotchet (one crotchet beat) 𝅘𝅥		Dotted minim (three crotchet beats) 𝅗𝅥.
	+		=	

1 Add the total number of crotchet beats in these note values.

½ + ½ + 1 + 2 = 4 crotchet beats
_____

𝅝 + 𝅗𝅥

= 6
_____

𝅗𝅥 + 𝅘𝅥

= 3
_____

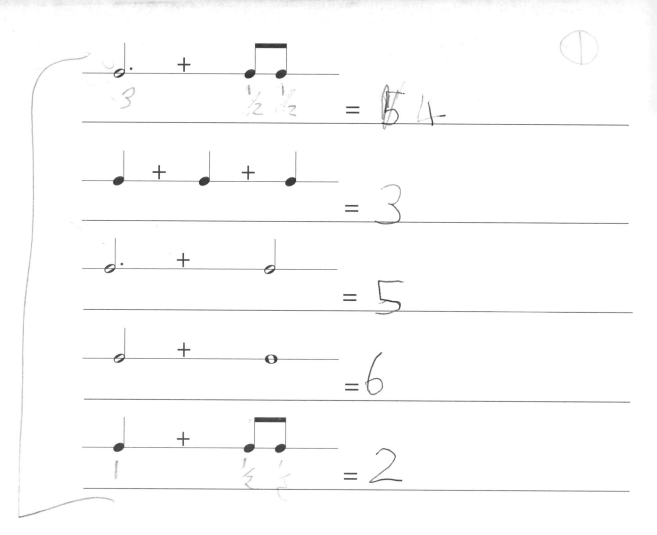

= 1

= 3

= 5

= 6

= 2

2 Write six crotchet **G**s.

3 Write three minim **E**s and two semibreve **D**s.

4 Write three dotted minim **F**s and two dotted minim **G**s.

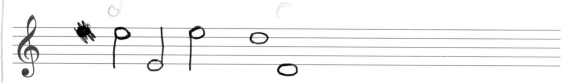

5 Write eight quavers on **C**, beamed together in twos.

Rests

Each silence within a piece of music lasts for a certain length of time and is called a **rest**. Musicians measure rests by feeling the number of silent regular beats within them. The beat used to measure rests in Grade 1 is the **crotchet**.

Rests are drawn in different ways to show how many beats to count while the silence lasts:

Semibreve rest   This rest lasts for four crotchet beats
                       or
                       a whole bar of silence in any time signature
                       (see page 36)

Minim rests   These rests last for two crotchet beats each

Crotchet rests   These rests last for one crotchet beat each

(crotchet beat)

A dot after a rest means that half its value again is added to its length. But for a rest lasting for three beats you write:

   not

When you first see minim and semibreve rests they look rather similar. Think 'semibreve submarine' and you will remember that the semibreve rest hangs down from the line.

 1 Write over the dotted lines to make crotchet rests. Draw them as one continuous line.

2 Match the following rests to the names that correctly describe their lengths.

semibreve rest

minim rest

crotchet rest

3 Match the length of the following note values to the rests.

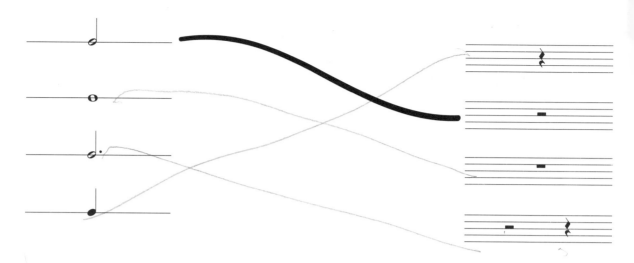

4 Add the total number of crotchet beats in these note values and rests.

ξ + o

___1___ + ___4___ = ___5 crotchet beats___

♩ + ♩ + ▬

= 4

♩. + ξ + ▬ + ♫
3   1   4   2

= 10

ξ + ξ + ♩ + ♩.
1   1   2   3

= 7

♫ + ♩. + ▬ + ξ
2   3   2   1

= 8

Bars, bar lines and time signatures

Beats are organised into **bars**, with a **bar line** at the end of each one. For Grade 1 bars can hold two, three or four crotchet beats. The first beat of the bar is a little stronger than the others and this adds a particular character to the music:

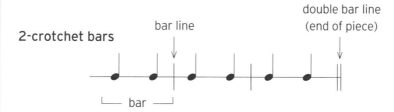

2-crotchet bars

3-crotchet bars

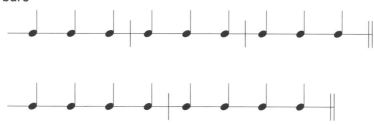

There is a **time signature** at the beginning of the music.

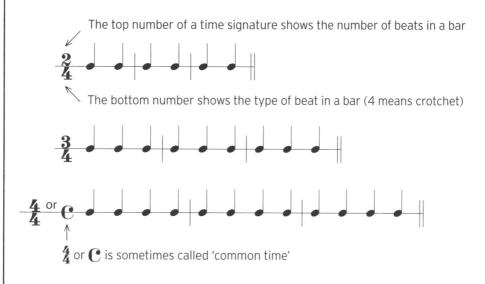

1 Write the correct time signatures.

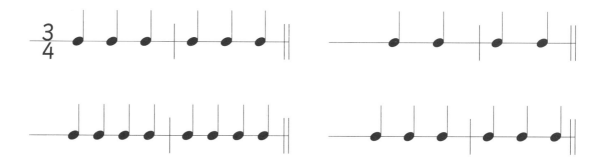

2 Write a treble clef and fill each bar with crotchets (**F**s and **C**s).

3 Write a bass clef and fill each bar with crotchets (**B**s and **G**s).

4 Write a bass clef and fill each bar with crotchets (two different **C**s).

5 Count up the number of crotchet beats in each first bar. In the second bar write one note **E** to show the total value of the notes and rests in the first bar.

6 Write the correct time signatures.

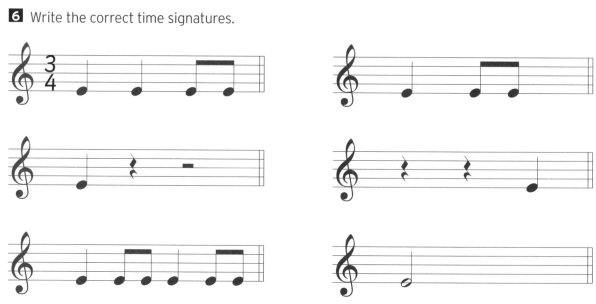

7 Look at the following music. Add bar lines to agree with the time signatures.

Tones and semitones

Did you know?

A scale usually moves up or down in steps. These steps are called **degrees**.

You will learn major scales on your instrument at first, but there are other types of scale too.

If you play all the white notes from **C** to **C** on a keyboard you will be playing the **scale of C major**:

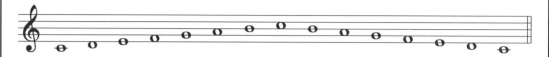

The distance between every white note and the next is not always the same:

– if a black note comes between them the distance is called a **tone**.

– if there is no black note between them the distance is called a **semitone** (meaning 'half a tone').

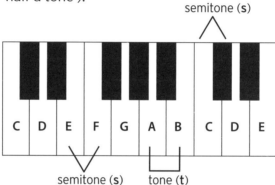

In other words, there is a distance of a semitone between every next-door note on the keyboard – black or white.

1 Look at the following pairs of notes and say whether the distance between them is a tone or a semitone. Check the clef each time.

Did you know?

If you are a string player you can feel the different distances between tones and semitones with your left-hand fingers. Ask your teacher to show you.

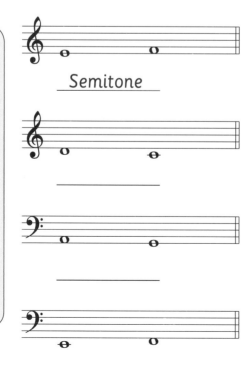

Semitone
_____

_____

_____

_____

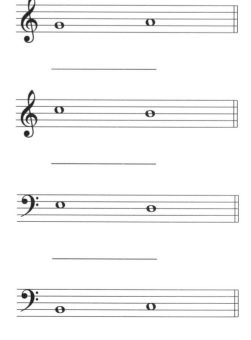

_____

_____

_____

_____

16

Accidentals

Handy tip!

Tilt the lines across the sharp sign so that it doesn't get muddled up with the stave lines and become difficult to read:

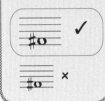

Accidentals are signs that are put just before a note to tell musicians to change the **pitch** (how high or low a sound is). The type of sign used shows how to change it.

The **flat** (♭) lowers the pitch by a semitone.

 ↓ pitch goes down from **B** to **B flat**

The **sharp** (♯) raises the pitch by a semitone.

 ↑ pitch goes up from **F** to **F sharp**

The **natural** (♮) cancels any previous sign.

 ↑ pitch goes up from **B flat** to **B natural** (by cancelling out the flat)

 ↓ pitch goes down from **F sharp** to **F natural** (by cancelling out the sharp)

An accidental lasts until another one on exactly the same line or space cancels it, or until the next bar line.

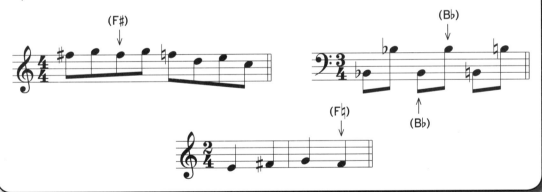

Did you know?

Quavers are sometimes beamed together in groups of four. Look at page 33 to find out why.

1 Write over the dotted lines to make flats, sharps and naturals.

Handy tip!

Write flat and natural signs in two parts:

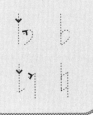

2 Write a flat in every space and a sharp on every line.

3 Write a flat just before these notes. Then write their note names.

Bb _____ _____ _____ _____

Handy tip!

Be sure to position accidentals carefully so that they apply to the correct note.

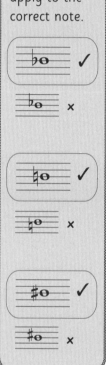

4 Write a sharp just before these notes. Then write their note names.

F# _____ _____ _____ _____

5 Write a natural just before these notes. Then write their note names.

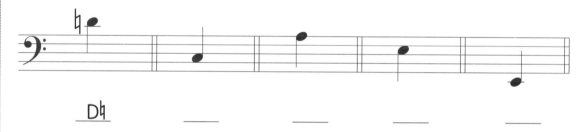

D♮ _____ _____ _____ _____

6 Flatten each middle note below. Then return it to its original pitch.

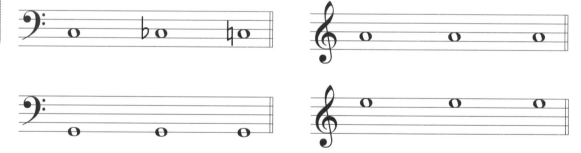

7 Sharpen each middle note below. Then return it to its original pitch.

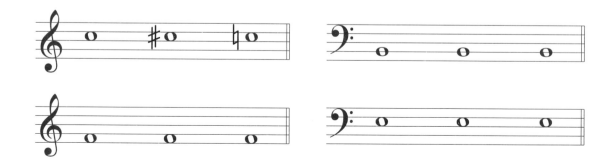

18

Keys – C major

If someone tells you that a piece of music is **in the key of C major**, it means that the music you hear will mostly use the notes from the scale of C major.

Within any key, the 1st degree of the scale (whatever the register) is the **tonic**. For Grade 1 you need to know that it can also be called **doh**. Tunes often begin and end on it with the result that the tonic sounds special.

Here is the scale of C major going up:

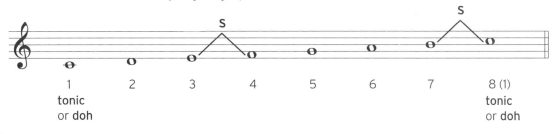

1 Answer the following questions:

- Give two possible names for the 1st degree in any key. <u>Tonic or doh</u>

- Which note is the tonic in the key of C major?_____

- If you write a piece in the key of C major, from which scale will you take most of the notes?

_____

- If you listen to a piece in the key of C major, on which note will the music often begin and end?

_____

- Write the scale of C major going up. Use semibreves and number the degrees of the scale.

- Circle the **C**s in the scale you have written above and label them doh.

2 Mark the semitones in the following music with a bracket (∧ or ∨) and an **S** for semitone.

The tonic triad in the key of C major

A **chord** is two or more notes played at the same time.
A **tonic triad** is a chord made up of the 1st, 3rd and 5th degrees of a scale.

Here is the scale of C major:

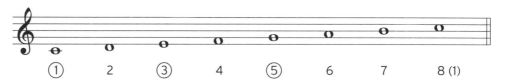

Here is the tonic triad in the key of C major:

Handy tip!
Play this triad so that you know how it sounds.

It is called a tonic triad in the key of C major because it is built on the 1st degree (the tonic) of the C major scale.

Often you will find a Roman numeral written below it (I), showing that the chord is built on the 1st degree of the scale.

Handy tip!
Write Roman numerals below the stave(s).

Composers (people who invent music) sometimes label the tonic triad in C major as **C** especially if they are writing **chord symbols** for guitar.

In fact any chord that uses just the notes of this triad (whatever the register) can have this label:

Handy tip!
Write chord symbols above the stave(s).

Chords and tunes that only use **C**, **E** and **G** fit together well – whether the chords or tunes are in the treble or the bass clef.

1 Add **E**s and **G**s to make tonic triads in the key of C major.

   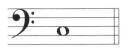

2 Add either **E** or **G** to make tonic triads in the key of C major.

   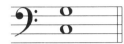

3 Look at the music below. It is all written using the notes of the tonic triad in the key of C major. Label the part that has the tune and the part that plays the chords.

Tune _____

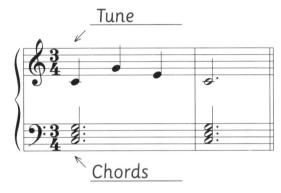 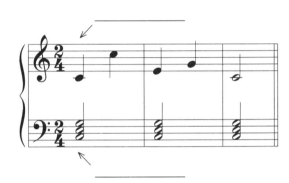

Chords _____

4 Using minims, write out the tonic triad in the key of C major. Choose which tonic to start on.

Other major keys – G and F

The key of C major is the only major key using just the white notes of the keyboard. In other keys sharps and flats need to be added to make the major-scale pattern of tones and semitones. In any major scale you will find semitones only between the 3rd & 4th and 7th & 8th degrees of the scale.

1 Look at the following scales and put a bracket (⋀ or ⋁) between the 3rd & 4th and 7th & 8th degrees of the scale. Then add any sharps or flats necessary to make these major scales.

Scale of G major

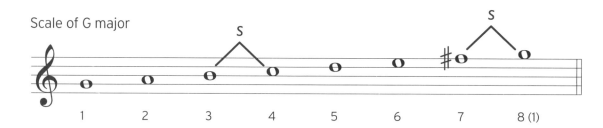

Did you know?

Degrees of the scale go 87654321 if the scale goes down.

Scale of F major

Scale of G major

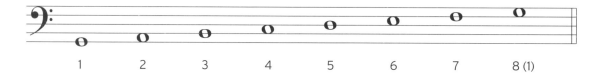

Scale of F major

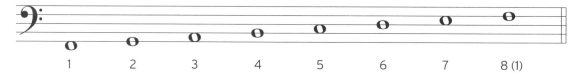

Scale of G major

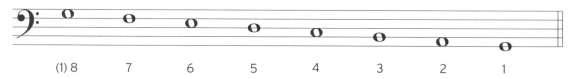

22

Key signatures

From your work on page 22 you will know that an **F sharp** is necessary in G major to make a semitone between the 7th & 8th degrees.

Pieces in the key of G major usually use **F sharps** all the way through. To keep things simple, composers use a **key signature** at the beginning of every stave to show the player that all the **F**s in the piece (whatever the register) are raised to **F sharp**.

See how this makes the music easier to read:

In the key of G major without a key signature:

In the key of G major with a key signature:

key signature (with a sharp on the line on which **F** sits)

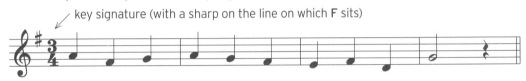

Notice that the key signature always appears just before the time signature.

Look at the position of flats or sharps in each of the key signatures below. They are always put in the same place.

Here are the Grade 1 key signatures:

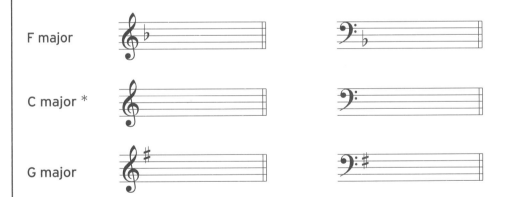

F major

C major *

G major

* No sharps or flats are needed to make the major-scale pattern of tones and semitones in the key of C major, so the key signature for C major has no sharps or flats.

Remember

Key signature flats or sharps apply to every note with the same note name (whatever the register).

1 Write the key signature for each key.

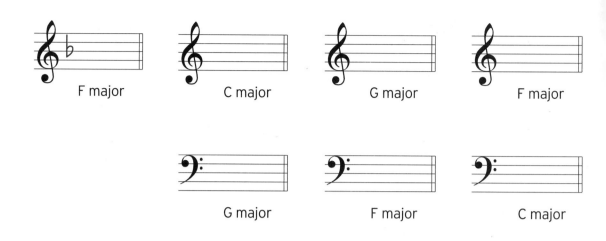

F major   C major   G major   F major

G major   F major   C major

2 Write in a semibreve tonic note (at any register) for the major key shown by the key signature.

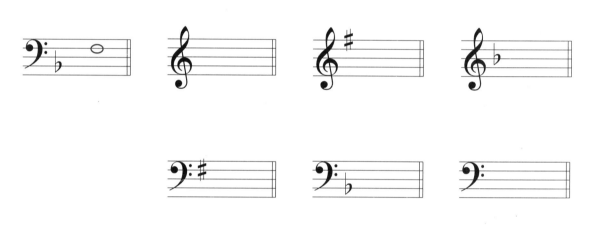

3 Write in semibreves the tonic triad for the major key shown by the key signature.

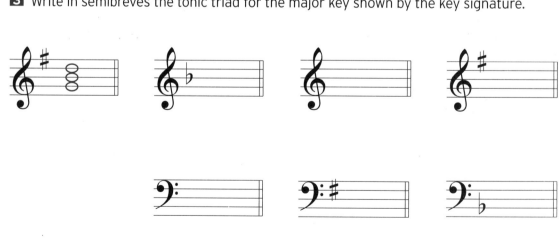

4 To which major keys do these tonic triads belong?

F major _____   _____   _____   _____

_____   _____   _____

Remember

In the key of G major the tonic chord can be labelled **I** or **G**.

In the key of F major the tonic chord can be labelled **I** or **F**.

5 Label these tonic triads using Roman numerals below the chord.

I

6 Label these tonic triads using chord symbols above the chord.

G

7 Write one-octave major scales in semibreves going up. Use key signatures and mark the semitones with a bracket (∧ or ∨) and an **S** for semitone.

Handy tip!

Write in the degrees of the scale if you find it useful so that you can check that there is a distance of a semitone between the 3rd & 4th and the 7th & 8th degrees.

C major

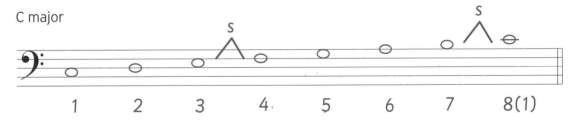

1   2   3   4   5   6   7   8(1)

G major

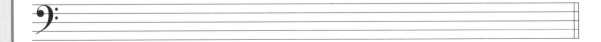

F major

8 Write one-octave major scales in semibreves going down. Use key signatures and mark the semitones with a bracket (∧ or ∨) and an **S** for semitone.

C major

G major

F major

9 Look at the key signatures to work out the major keys.

Haydn

etc.

This music is in the key of ___F major___

Traditional

This music is in the key of _____

Mozart

etc.

This music is in the key of _____

10 No key signatures have been used here. Look at the accidentals and work out the keys.

Beethoven

The key is ___F major___

Albéniz

The key is _____

Elgar

The key is _____

Beethoven

The key is _____

Haydn

etc.

The key is _____

Intervals

An **interval** is the distance between two notes.
To find an interval count up from the bottom note like this:

This interval is a **5th**.

There are only two intervals that are not usually known by a number:

− **unison** (where both notes sound the same):

These notes are in **unison**.

or

− an **octave** (an 8th). This is the distance between any note and the next note with the same letter name:

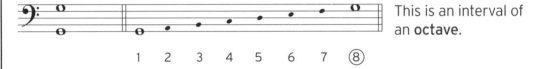

This is an interval of an **octave**.

1 Name the following intervals by counting up the notes.

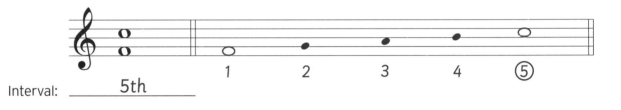

Interval: _____5th_____

Interval: _____

Interval: _____

Interval: _____

Here are the types of intervals that you will need to know for Grade 1:

| Unison | 2nd | 3rd | 4th | 5th | Octave |

To make an interval of unison, a 3rd or a 5th, the notes always have to be written *either* on lines *or* in spaces.

For example:

or

2nds, 4ths and octaves are different; it is always necessary to use a line *and* a space.

For example:

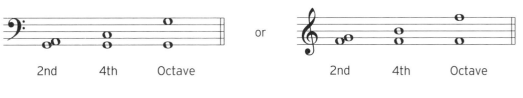

or

Remember

Count up from the bottom note.

2 Name the following intervals by counting up the notes.

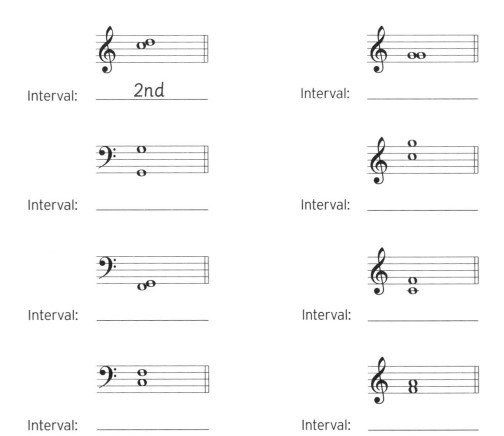

Interval: _____2nd_____

Interval: _____

Interval: _____

Interval: _____

Interval: _____

Interval: _____

Interval: _____

Interval: _____

The circle of 5ths

The **circle of 5ths** is a map of the keys used in music. It helps you find out how many sharps or flats there are in any key signature. The highlighted keys are the only keys that you will need to know for Grade 1.

Take time to understand how it works because it will be very useful as you move up the grades.

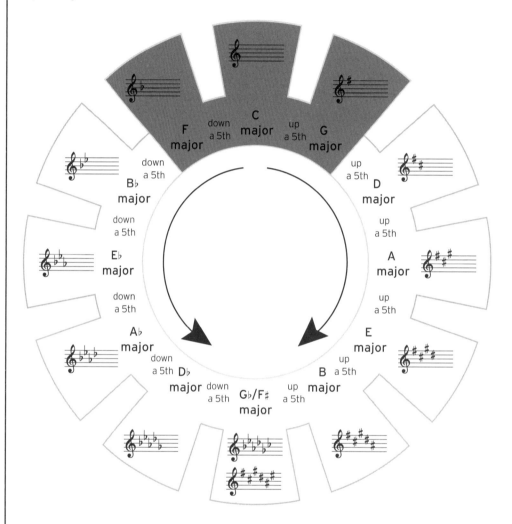

Did you know?

The remainder of the circle works in the same way. As you go through the grades you will learn more of the keys around the circle.

Start at C major. To find the major key with one sharp in its key signature just move round one notch to the right (or up a 5th from **C**) and the answer is there: G major.

To find a major key with one flat in its key signature just move round one notch to the left (or down a 5th from **C**). The answer is F major.

Arpeggios

Here is the tonic triad in the key of F major:

An **arpeggio** is made by 'breaking up' a chord like this and playing it as a tune.

Here is the type of arpeggio that you need to know for Grade 1 – it is a one-octave arpeggio (shown here in the key of F major).

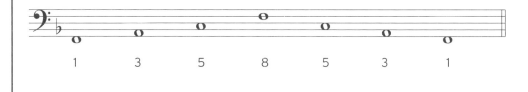

1   3   5   8   5   3   1

1   3   5   8   5   3   1

1 Using semibreves, write the following tonic triads and one-octave arpeggios (going up then down), using the correct key signature each time.

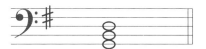

Tonic triad in the key of G major

One-octave arpeggio in the key of G major

Tonic triad in the key of F major

One-octave arpeggio in the key of F major

Tonic triad in the key of C major

One-octave arpeggio in the key of C major

Tonic triad in the key of G major

One-octave arpeggio in the key of G major

31

2 Using semibreves, write the following tonic triads and one-octave arpeggios (going down then up), using the correct key signature each time.

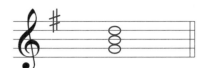

Tonic triad in the key of G major

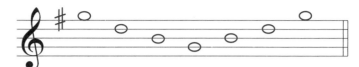

One-octave arpeggio in the key of G major

Tonic triad in the key of F major

One-octave arpeggio in the key of F major

Tonic triad in the key of C major

One-octave arpeggio in the key of C major

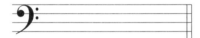

Tonic triad in the key of G major

One-octave arpeggio in the key of G major

3 Put a bracket (⌐‾ or ⌐_) to show any complete one-octave arpeggios hidden in the music. Then name the arpeggio.

C major arpeggio going up

etc.

_____

etc.

_____

_____

Grouping notes and beaming quavers

When a composer writes two quavers to be played in one crotchet beat they are usually grouped together with a thick line called a **beam**. Joining up quavers like this is called **beaming**:

When a composer writes four quavers to be played in two next-door crotchet beats, it is normal for these notes to be beamed together, for example:

1 Fill the coloured boxes with correctly beamed quavers to complete the bars.

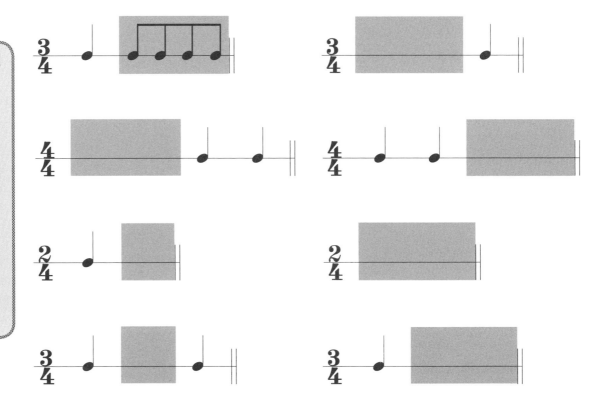

Beaming quavers in $\frac{4}{4}$

In a $\frac{4}{4}$ bar, imagine a hidden barrier between beats 1 & 2 and 3 & 4. Never cross the barrier by beaming beats 2 and 3 together.

2 Fill in the coloured boxes with correctly beamed quavers to complete the bars.

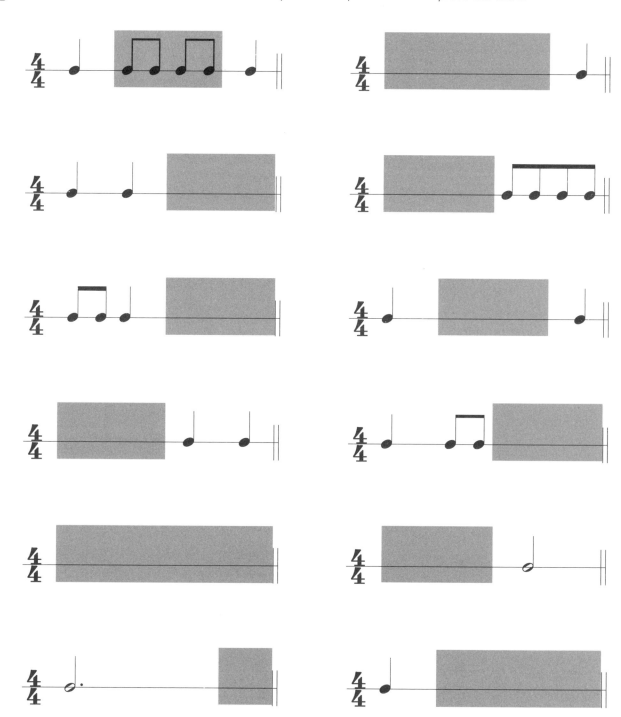

Beaming a full bar of quavers in $\frac{3}{4}$

When a composer writes six quavers to be played in a $\frac{3}{4}$ bar they are normally beamed together.

3 Fill in the coloured boxes with correctly beamed quavers to complete the bars.

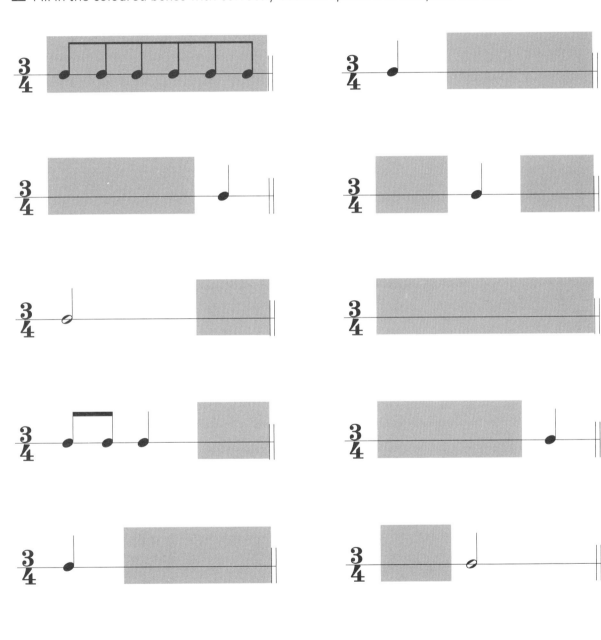

Grouping rests

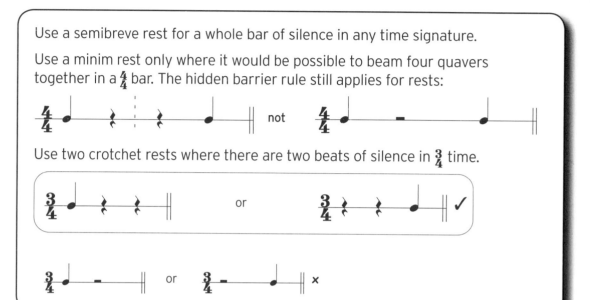

Did you know?

Semibreve rests are usually put in the middle of any empty bar.

1 Fill the coloured boxes with correctly grouped rests to complete the bars.

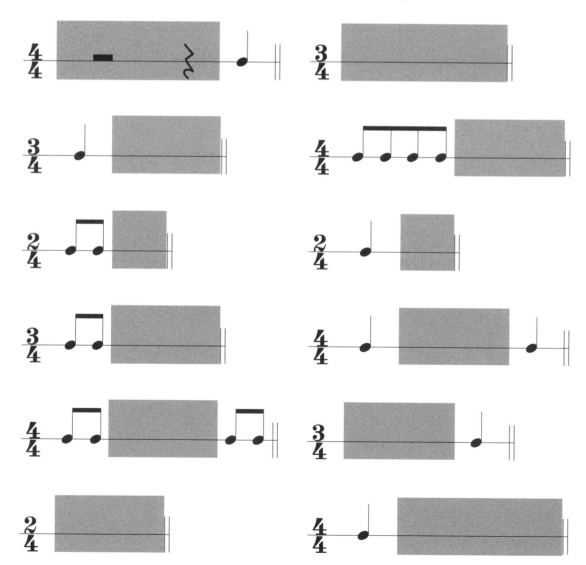

2 The following music contains mistakes in the grouping of notes and rests. Write it out correctly.

Handel

etc.

Traditional

etc.

Handel

etc.

Haydn

etc.

3 The following music contains a lot of different mistakes. Write it out correctly.

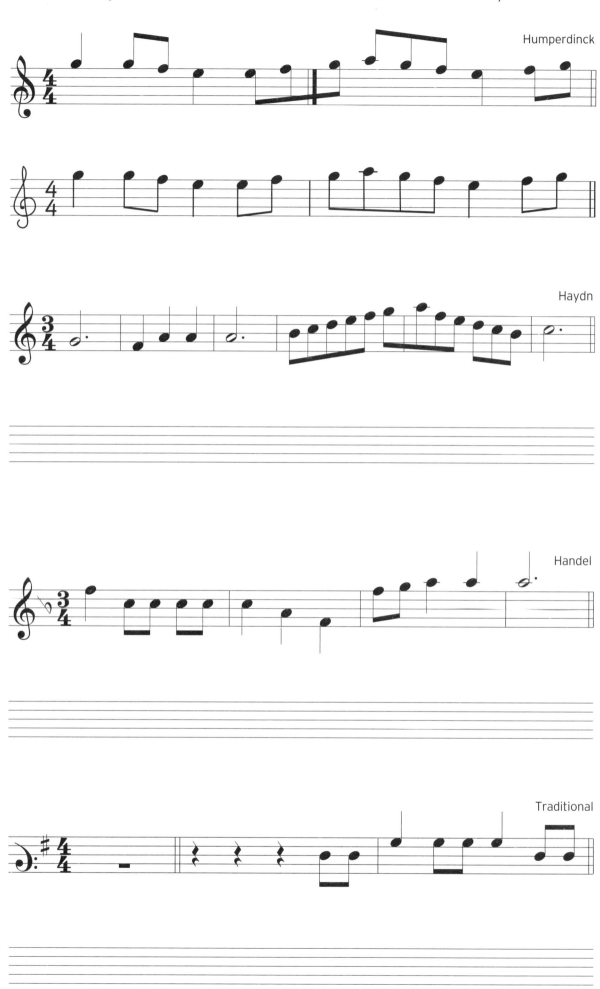

Humperdinck

Haydn

Handel

Traditional

Answering a given rhythm

Here is a 2-bar rhythm:

Handy tip!
Tap both rhythms to feel the difference for yourself.

To make a 4-bar rhythm, it could be answered like this:

or like this:

The second answer is better because it uses part of the original rhythm without copying it completely and feels finished at the end.

or like this:

The third answer is even better because as well as using part of the original rhythm, it also shows variety.

1 Answer the following rhythms.

Handy tip!
Rhythms may also include rests.

Ostinato

Did you know?

Ostinati is the plural of ostinato.

An **ostinato** is a pattern of notes (written in a certain rhythm) that repeats over and over again in a piece. The pattern can be short (just a few notes) or long. Ostinati are often used to accompany tunes and appear in lots of rap and other kinds of pop music.

1 Look at the following ostinati and bracket (⌐‾¬ or ∟__⌐) each repeat of the pattern.

2 Here are some ostinati. Write two more repeats of each pattern.

Did you know?

Ostinati often include chords.

Musical words and symbols

A written piece of music can contain lots of information – not just the notes to be played and in what rhythm, but **how** to play them.

For Grade 1 you need to know the following:

Dynamic markings
(tell a player how loudly or softly to play)

pianissimo (*pp*) – very soft

piano (*p*) – soft

mezzo piano (*mp*) – medium soft (*mezzo* means half)

mezzo forte (*mf*) – medium loud

forte (*f*) – loud

fortissimo (*ff*) – very loud

crescendo (*cresc.* or ———————) – getting gradually louder

diminuendo (*dim.* or ———————) – getting gradually softer

Articulation marks
(tell a player how to play the notes, e.g. smoothly or with an accent)

> (accent) – play with an accent

legato – play smoothly

♪ ♪ ♪ (slur) – play the marked notes smoothly

♩ ♩ (*staccato*) – play these notes detached, short and crisp

Tempo marks and other signs
(tell a player what speed to play the music and other details)

Andante – at a walking pace

Allegro – fast

Moderato – at a moderate pace

ritenuto (*rit.*) – getting slower

‖: and/or :‖ (repeat marks) – repeat the section or repeat from the beginning of the piece

---

Handy tip!

Dynamics are usually put below the music. Often abbreviations are used, not the full word, e.g. *f* not *forte*.

Did you know?

Articulation marks are usually put close to the note-heads.

Handy tip!

Tempo marks are usually put above the music at the beginning of a piece.

1 Show that this music should be played at a walking pace. Add dynamics to show that it should be played softly. In bar 3 it should get louder. In bar 4 it should be loud.

2 Show that this music should be played fast. Add dynamics to show that it should be played very loudly. In bar 3 it should get softer.

3 Show that this music should be played at a moderate pace. Add dynamics to show that it should be played medium loud. Add an accent to the first note of each bar. Then add a repeat sign to show that this music should be repeated.

4 Show that this music should be played fast and loud. Add *staccato* marks to all the quavers.

5 Show that this music should be played at a walking pace and very soft. Add three-note slurs above the bars where there are crotchet note values.

6 Show that this music should be played at a moderate pace and soft. Show that it should be played smoothly.

Analysis

Analysis means looking at a piece of music carefully and noticing how it is composed. This will help you to get more out of listening to music. It will also help you to play your instrument (or sing) more convincingly because you will understand how the music is put together.

1 Look at the following piece and answer the questions below.

Did you know?

Bar 1 is not usually numbered; the number is included here to make it easy to find the bar you need.

Did you know?

An **accompaniment** is music that supports (or backs) a tune.

1. In which major key is this piece? __F major__

2. What note is the tonic in this piece? __F__

3. Write a Roman numeral below the last note of this piece to show that the tonic triad should accompany it.

4. How many crotchet beats are there in each bar? __2__

5. Put a bracket (⌐‾⌐) above the place where there is a one-octave scale in the key of the piece.

6. Is this scale going up or down? __Going down__

7. Put *staccato* marks on all the quavers.

8. How should *staccato* notes be played? __Detached, short and crisp__

9. What does **Allegro** mean? __Play the music fast__

10. At what dynamic should a musician start to play this piece? __Softly__

11. What does 𝄇 mean? __Repeat the piece from the beginning__

12. Name the interval between the two notes marked with asterisks (*) in bar 1. __2nd__

13. What does ◁‾‾‾‾ mean? __Getting gradually louder__

14. Write the lowest and highest notes in this piece as crotchets:

15. Name the interval between the lowest and highest notes in this piece.

__An octave__

43

2 Look at the following piece and answer the questions below.

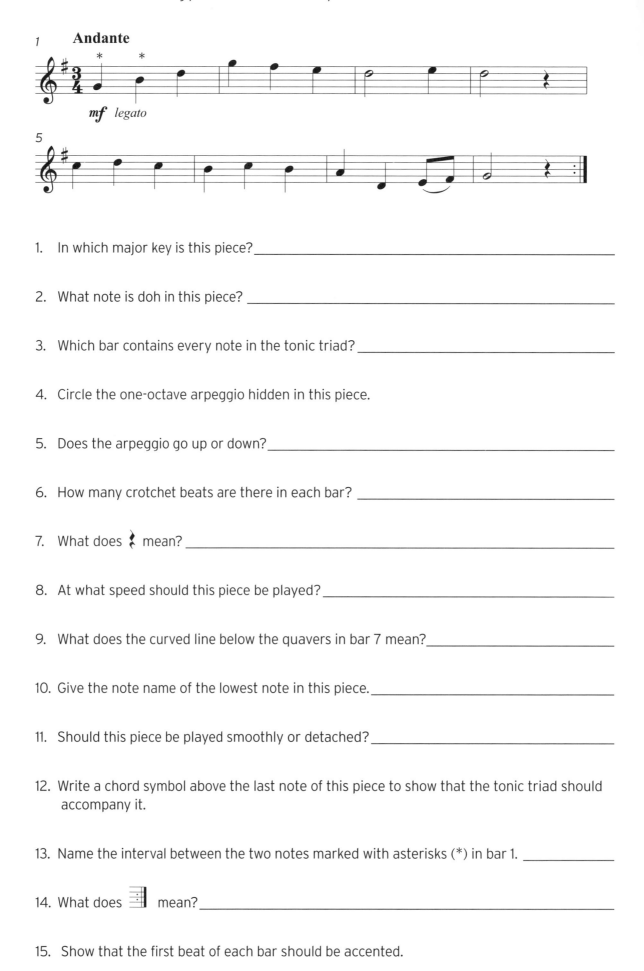

1. In which major key is this piece?_____

2. What note is doh in this piece? _____

3. Which bar contains every note in the tonic triad?_____

4. Circle the one-octave arpeggio hidden in this piece.

5. Does the arpeggio go up or down?_____

6. How many crotchet beats are there in each bar? _____

7. What does 𝄽 mean? _____

8. At what speed should this piece be played?_____

9. What does the curved line below the quavers in bar 7 mean?_____

10. Give the note name of the lowest note in this piece._____

11. Should this piece be played smoothly or detached?_____

12. Write a chord symbol above the last note of this piece to show that the tonic triad should accompany it.

13. Name the interval between the two notes marked with asterisks (*) in bar 1. _____

14. What does ⊟ mean?_____

15. Show that the first beat of each bar should be accented.

3 Look at the following piece and answer the questions below.

1. In which major key is this piece? _____

2. What note is the tonic in this piece? _____

3. The tonic is written in two registers in this piece.
    Put a box (▢) around an example of a low and high tonic.

4. Put a bracket (⌐¬) above the place where there is a one-octave scale in the key of the piece.

5. Is this scale going up or down? _____

6. At what tempo should this piece be played? _____

7. How many crotchet beats are there in each bar? _____

8. How many crotchet beats are there in the note in bar 8? _____

9. What does the curved line over the first two crotchets in bar 3 mean?_____

10. What does the dynamic marking in bar 1 mean? _____

11. Write a chord symbol above the last note of this piece to show that the tonic triad should accompany it.

12. Name the interval between the two notes marked with asterisks (*) in bar 1. _____

13. Is the distance between the last two notes a tone or a semitone? _____

14. What does ⫞ mean?_____

15. What does 𝄽 mean? _____

4 Look at the following piece and answer the questions below.

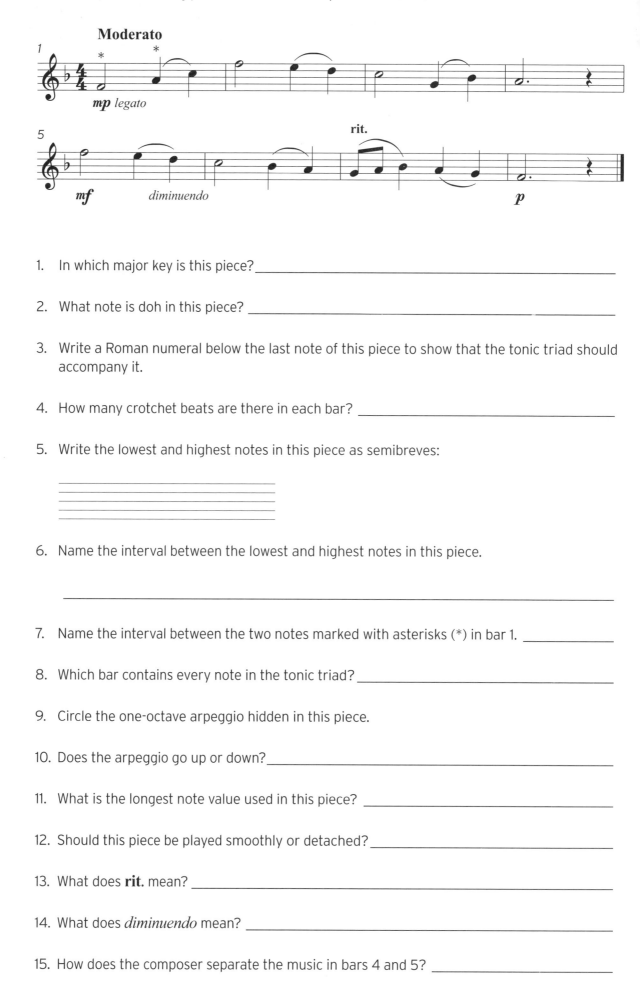

1. In which major key is this piece?_____

2. What note is doh in this piece? _____ _____

3. Write a Roman numeral below the last note of this piece to show that the tonic triad should accompany it.

4. How many crotchet beats are there in each bar? _____

5. Write the lowest and highest notes in this piece as semibreves:

6. Name the interval between the lowest and highest notes in this piece.

   _____

7. Name the interval between the two notes marked with asterisks (*) in bar 1. _____

8. Which bar contains every note in the tonic triad? _____

9. Circle the one-octave arpeggio hidden in this piece.

10. Does the arpeggio go up or down?_____

11. What is the longest note value used in this piece? _____

12. Should this piece be played smoothly or detached?_____

13. What does **rit.** mean? _____

14. What does *diminuendo* mean? _____

15. How does the composer separate the music in bars 4 and 5? _____

    _____

Sample examination paper

Section 1 (20 marks)

Put a tick (✓) in the box next to the correct answer.

Example

Name this note:

A ☐   D ☐   C ☑

This shows that you think **C** is the correct answer.

1.1   Name this note:

G ☐   B ☐   E ☐

1.2   Name this note:

B flat ☐   G flat ☐   G sharp ☐

1.3   Name the notes to find the hidden word:

CAFE ☐   FADE ☐   FACE ☐

1.4   How many crotchet beats are there in a crotchet?

2 ☐   1 ☐   3 ☐

1.5   Add the total number of crotchet beats in these note values and rests.

4 ☐   5 ☐   6 ☐

Put a tick (✓) in the box next to the correct answer.

1.6 Which rest matches the length of this note value?

      𝄽 ☐   ▬ ☐   ▬ ☐

1.7 Which is the correct time signature?

      $\frac{3}{4}$ ☐ $\frac{4}{4}$ ☐ $\frac{2}{4}$ ☐

1.8 To raise the pitch of this note by a semitone, which accidental would you put just before it?

      ♮ ☐   ♭ ☐   ♯ ☐

1.9 Which pair of notes has a distance of a semitone between them?

      A and B ☐   A and B♭ ☐   D and C ☐

1.10 Which note is doh in the key of G major?   F ☐   C ☐   G ☐

1.11 Here is the scale of C major. Where are the semitones?

(1)8   7   6   5   4   3   2   1

    Between the 2nd & 3rd degrees ☐

    Between the 7th & 8th degrees ☐

Between the 3rd & 4th degrees and the 7th & 8th degrees ☐

48

Put a tick (✓) in the box next to the correct answer.

1.12 Which major key has the following key signature?

C major ☐   F major ☐   G major ☐

☐

1.13 Which symbol does **not** fit with this tonic triad?

C ☐   I ☐   F ☐

☐

1.14 Which note needs to be added to make a tonic triad in the key of G major?

G ☐   B ☐   F ☐

☐

1.15 Name this interval:

Unison ☐   2nd ☐   3rd ☐

☐

1.16 Name this interval:

3rd ☐   4th ☐   5th ☐

☐

1.17 A dot after a note means:

that the note should be played staccato ☐
that the note should be played smoothly ☐
that half its value again is added to its length ☐

☐

1.18 Which notes would you find in the tonic triad in the key of F major?

FAD ☐   FAC ☐   FGA ☐

☐

1.19 What does *legato* mean?

play smoothly ☐   very soft ☐   getting gradually louder ☐

☐

1.20 What does *pianissimo* mean?

very soft ☐   play on the piano ☐   medium soft ☐

☐

Section 2 (20 marks)

Write the following, using key signatures.

2.1 A one-octave F major scale in semibreves going up. Mark the semitones with a bracket
($\wedge$ or $\vee$) and an **S** for semitone.

2.2 A one-octave arpeggio of G major in semibreves going up then down.

Section 3 (15 marks)

3.1 Circle five different mistakes in the following music, then write it out correctly.

Section 4 (15 marks)

4.1   Answer the following rhythm.

Section 5 (10 marks)

5.1   Here is an ostinato. Write two more repeats of the pattern.

Please turn over for Section 6

Section 6 (20 marks)

Look at the following piece and answer the questions below.

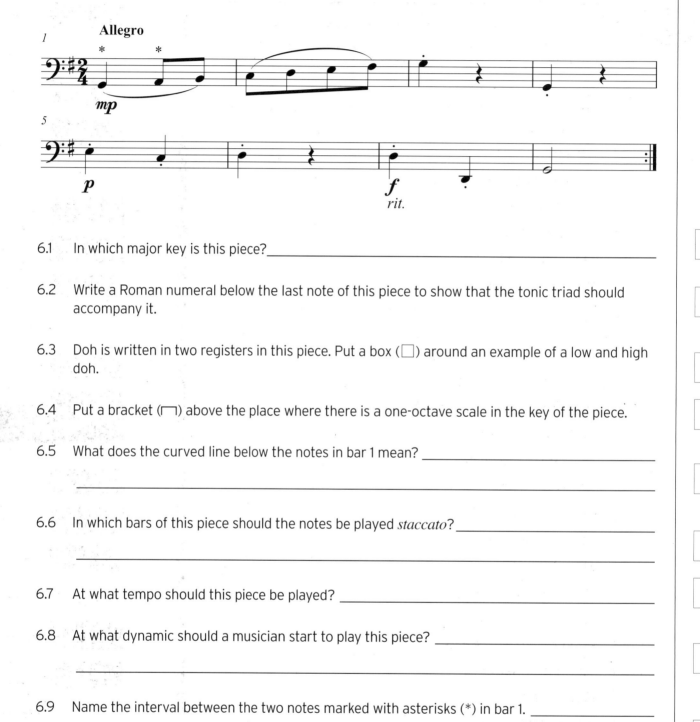

6.1   In which major key is this piece?_____

6.2   Write a Roman numeral below the last note of this piece to show that the tonic triad should accompany it.

6.3   Doh is written in two registers in this piece. Put a box (☐) around an example of a low and high doh.

6.4   Put a bracket (⌐⌐) above the place where there is a one-octave scale in the key of the piece.

6.5   What does the curved line below the notes in bar 1 mean? _____

_____

6.6   In which bars of this piece should the notes be played *staccato*? _____

_____

6.7   At what tempo should this piece be played? _____

6.8   At what dynamic should a musician start to play this piece? _____

_____

6.9   Name the interval between the two notes marked with asterisks (*) in bar 1. _____

_____

6.10   What does *rit.* mean? _____

_____